AYA:

AN ANTHOLOGY OF RACIAL JUSTICE, HEALING AND THE BLACK EXPERIENCE

Planting People Growing Justice Press
P.O. Box 131894
Saint Paul, MN 55113
www.ppgjbooks.com

Printed and bound in the United States of America
First Edition
LCCN: 2022944941
SC ISBN: 978-1-959223-90-0

TABLE OF CONTENTS

ABOUT AYA

AYA (pronounced as "eye–ah") is part of adinkra—visual symbols linked to the (former) Gyaman kingdom and Ashanti culture. Aya translates as "fern" and symbolizes endurance, resourcefulness, and defiance against oppression.

Aya embodies Planting People Growing Justice's commitment to bring about racial justice and healing. It offers an opportunity to pause, reflect, and grow through the transformative power of the arts and humanities. In partnership with LiLu Interiors, Aya's Place was founded to create a space for the Black community to connect with their inner artist and reimagine themselves and the world with clarity. Humanity needs the artist within as much as the leader within if we are to put an end to systemic racism and create a just and equitable world.

The theme of this anthology aligns with the vision of Aya's Place. It was produced in partnership with Saint Paul youth and community activists.

ABOUT PLANTING PEOPLE GROWING JUSTICE LEADERSHIP INSTITUTE

Planting People Growing Justice Leadership Institute seeks to plant seeds of social change through education, training, and community outreach.

All proceeds from this book will support the educational programming of the Planting People Growing Justice Leadership Institute.

Learn more at www.ppgjli.org.

This activity is made possible through a grant from the Saint Paul Star Program.

LETTER FROM THE EDITOR

Third Reconstruction, Racial Reckoning—none of these words could fully encapsulate the reality of the quest for justice. On May 25, 2020, Mr. George Floyd was murdered in Minneapolis, Minnesota. Darnella Frazier captured the last moments of Floyd's life in a video recording that went viral. Millions around the world watched the video, which compelled them to take action.

Each of us was left with a decision of whether we would remain on the sidelines of life as passive observers. The decision was individual and personal, but a decision had to be made. It was a moment in history that ignited a movement. Every day, people decided to bring the issues of justice to the forefront of the national agenda related to racial justice. The inequities could no longer be ignored and were placed center stage.

The future was awaiting us. The work of the present was still undone. My home state of Minnesota, like countless others across the nation, faced a similar challenge. A tale of two cities was no longer a tale of fiction but a lived reality. One experienced great prosperity and immense joy while another was left in abject poverty and experiencing insurmountable despair. One was white. One was Black. Separate and unequal. This is a reality when in Minnesota:

- Wealth: The Black poverty rate is four times the white poverty rate.
- Education: Black students experience one of the nation's worst education opportunity gaps, as evidenced by graduation and literacy rates.

A leadership challenge emerged—what will you do for justice and freedom? Or what is in your hands to make a difference in the world? I decided to take action by joining with other writers and artists to lead change. We came together to create and build a collective vision for the future. We envisioned a world where the sanctity of life was paramount and the promotion of the common good would be our guiding light. This vision compelled us to act together in building a vision for the future. This youth anthology is a manifestation of the vision. We visited St. Paul schools and community centers to encourage our youth to share their reflections on racial justice, healing, and the Black experience. They taught us key lessons on how to lead, inspire, and build a movement for racial justice. This youth anthology is a tableau of United States at a pivotal crossroad on the journey to racial justice. Our youth shall lead us...

Dr. Artika R. Tyner, Editor
Planting People Growing Justice Leadership Institute

RACIAL JUSTICE

Racial justice is the protection of the rights of Black people and fair treatment under the law.

#HASHTAGHEARTBREAK

VERONICA N. CHAPMAN

We should be safe in our Black bodies

Nourished in our mother's womb

Our beautifully designed vessels for our soul

Place where our purpose and promise are housed

Over which our ancestors watch

Over which our loved ones have prayed or chanted, and rubbed oils

Over which our village must too often mourn

And then rise in defiance

Diaspora in alliance

Against this common enemy

The fool's errand, to uphold white supremacy

Moving throughout the world like a twister

Pillaging and destroying everything in its wake

Destined to fail

#HashtagHeartbreak because the list keeps growing

This twisted trivia, how many can you name?

Our bodies we reclaim

White pathology stuck like glue,

We don't belong to you

#HashtagHeartbreak because we are tired

#HashtagHeartbreak because we never get time to heal

#HashtagHeartbreak because the world needs us

#HashtagHeartbreak because Black excellence is real

We deserve to grow old

WHAT COLOR IS FREEDOM?

KEVIN L REESE

What Color is Freedom?

Take a moment: if freedom was a color, what does it look like to you? I write this from the other side of my rainbow; over the years I have seen an array of colors and each one of those colors has taught me something, brought me something different.

I remember being a Black youth in America growing up in the '90s. My family was poor, so everything looked gray to me. Before social media and the internet, we watched sitcoms and traveled to other worlds for thirty minutes. Eight of those minutes were filled with commercials of kids in homes that didn't look like mine, playing with toys I felt I could never have, and enjoying life in a way I could only wish to. The other twenty-two minutes featured characters with clean clothes, clean homes, and problems answered by the end of the episode. I was green with envy; I did not wish to have a problem-free life, only for a clean home and clean clothes to face my problems in. This green envy manifested as red trauma, and this trauma spilled out anytime I lost the words to speak. I would speak red anger. This anger was classified, mostly by folks with blonde hair and blue eyes, looking at me from across their desks, branding my anger as a problem. All I thought in these moments was, "What do they know?" I imagine their houses are clean. These conversations always made me feel brown: dirty in comparison to them.

I was a child during the boom of mass incarceration, and the birth of the prison-to-school pipeline, which was introduced to me like the color of an icicle. I slid from detention as a youth to incarceration as a teen, where I would sit with no commercial breaks until I was a thirty-two-year-old man. These years are the color of stainless steel and crimson. Each day was beige, and with each step I took around the prison yard, my brown skin turned blacker. This forced my brown-eye pupils on themselves, where I saw only the surrounding whiteness determining every color I see.

Race is a man-made idea, rooted in a lie that says the color of your skin determines your cleanliness and worthiness. I have experienced gray, green, red, blonde, blue, brown, icicle, stainless steel, crimson, beige, black, and white. All real colors, but none of them me. I am a human being the color of the universe in which all things are possible. Kevin Reese is possible. I am someone who started his own business right from prison. Until We Are All Free was formed by a stainless-steel toilet, on a beige day, with crimson-stained hands. It is my life's work which gives me purpose the color of gold and led me here, writing to you. Hopefully these colors ricochet off whatever color your freedom is and remind you to color your own universe and create a world where everything is possible.

MY LIFE AS A BLACK PERSON

SERENITY SALTERS

I am Serenity Salters. I come from Minnesota. When you look at me, you see a young light-skinned girl. What you don't see is who I really am and what I've gone through. What stresses me out is knowing that Black people aren't treated the same, that every time I walk out of my house, there's a chance that I will be looked at differently or treated differently. I take care of myself by knowing that life has a chance to change, that life will be different. Healing, to me, is music. Justice, to me, is people who are white believing us and not just believing white people because they're white. Freedom, to me, is being able to go to a store or a restaurant and be treated with the same energy, not for the people there to only treat the white people with like a happy expression, and not for them to come to us with a bored expression and their answers to questions be something like "yep" or some short response. My wish for my community is that people of every race are treated the same and that we don't have to hear about white cops killing Black people when they didn't do anything and them getting away with it because their excuse was "I felt threatened" and because the jury was white.

RACIAL HEALING

Racial healing offers hope for the future and unlocks Black joy.

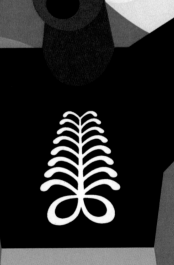

ALL OUT OF BREATH

DR. ARTIKA TYNER

Start with being centered and grounded.

Now, begin with a deep breath.

Inhale up, exhale down.

My mind begins to wonder—is breathing a privilege?

Who has access? When? How? Where?

Is a breath a luxury for some?

Is it a necessity for all?

Inhale up, exhale down.

What about Eric Garner?

Inhale up, exhale down.

"I can't breathe," George Floyd cried out.

Inhale up, exhale down.

Now, take a deep breath, hold it, and exhale peace and joy.

I do not have any peace and joy left.

Instead, I take a few deep breaths that fill my lungs with the anguish of pain and trauma.

What do you want to get out of this week?

I do not count weeks anymore.

1440, I can only count each precious minute.

Inhale up, exhale down.

I answer with a call to humanity.

How do we democratize a single breath?

Inhale up, exhale down.

It's hard to stay focused with each inhale when I realize that I am all out of breath.

HEAL THE ROOT

LATRESE JOHNSON

i am latrese. a descendent of
captive africans. i am an old soul
with a young body. the past and
the future. i'm someone whose
black is queer. i'm proof that we
are our own liberators. i'm healing
the root so the tree thrives. i am
an explorer. an anxious shape
shifter. youth activist. human
being. i come from the ancient red
dirt of west africa. grandmothers
that manifested my reality. i
come from those who fought
for us to get free. i come from
intersectional identities. when
you look at me, you see the child
no one had to worry about. what
you don't see is the things i do to
pour into myself. blasting music
to let the vibrations shatter my
trauma like glass. you don't see
my journey. healing is not linear.
it's uncomfortable. it requires me
to confront my limiting beliefs
and find liberating ones instead.
i'm healing the root so the tree
thrives. just like me, you don't
see social justice for the people.
and just like me, you don't see
social justice for the people. what
we need is healing justice and
peace and to hold space for each
other to grow. my hope for my
community is that we make it to
destination freedom. because i
have to, i believe we will make it
to destination freedom.

THAT BLACK CHILD
LYRIC M. HIGGINS

That black child

She will love herself

She will be thankful

She will be ok

She will be safe

She will be happy

She will be calm

She will be loved

She will be fed

She will be the person you thought she never would be

She will be strong and you will have to look up to me and have regret in your eyes and be sorry you spent your life looking down on me.

SPILLED INK, WORN-OUT SOLES, AND FLOWER BUDS: RACIAL HEALING AND THE BLACK EXPERIENCE

SALMA EGAL

When I sat down and started writing, I was struck with a feeling I wasn't familiar with. I didn't know what to say, or rather, write. It wasn't because I never thought about the Black experience; in fact, it is all I think about. All I can, because ever since I was born, my life was dutifully surrounded around my skin color.

I began writing but no words were produced. I even tried switching to my favorite bright pink ink. It's lucky, I thought. Instead, my fingers moved and formed a dance. I was in a trance. I watched incomprehensible words come out, in multiple languages. Somali, my parents' mother language, Spanish, my second language, even Arabic, a language I have only seen in the Quran. I watched stars and flowers appear, thorns and blood. At once, I understood my own Black experience.

So allow me to translate my dance, my silent language.

Sitting on a creaky desk, holding onto a new Hello Kitty backpack, lies Salma Egal, nervously awaiting her first day of kindergarten. She remembered this day all too well. Not because she had her favorite breakfast, a blueberry muffin with a glass of milk, or because she discovered that her best friend, a white girl who wore black glasses, was in her class. No, it was because she looked around and saw no one. I mean, she saw people, around 100, her five-year-old mind thought. But, she didn't see herself; unconsciously, she scanned the crowd and came up blank. She was the only Black person in her class. In fact, as she later figured out, Salma Egal was one of the six Black people in her grade. That same day, a white boy with blonde hair and blue eyes came up to her. "My mom doesn't like people who are Black," he said matter-of-factly. She crumbled inside.

Spilled ink. One only needs a slight push to be ruined.

Salma Egal grew accustomed to racism, so accustomed that she was no longer surprised. Still extremely hurt, but not surprised. She was merely five when she was forced to put on the big-girl pants, to hold the adult scissors—to hell with the ugly safety ones. She hated her skin and her curls and her ever-present yet non-existent accent. She hated it all. She heard boys giggle while screaming the n-word, teachers doubting her every move, counselors telling her that same phrase—"It's just not that big of a deal"—and girls staring at her with that same judgy look.

Salma grew accustomed to the death of a neighbor, a child, a father, a friend, all by the hands of people her teachers swear are to protect. She saw her dad get handcuffed for going five over, her cousin for "fitting the description." She saw white supremacists raid her hometown, her so-called friends turn their backs. She saw her Black classmates leave school one by one, dropping as if they were nothing but flies. She saw blood and stars and pretty white roses with ugly thorns that pricked her black fingers and—

She experienced self-hatred, grief, confusion, envy, and so much more before she went to her first homecoming. In fact, as Salma is writing this, she has yet to experience a homecoming.

Worn-out soles. Walked too much with brand-new shoes.

Salma, like so many other young Black folks, grew up way too fast.

She was five—no, seven—no, twelve, thirteen, fourteen, fifteen wearing a size sixteen when she was a size six. Her beautiful black skin was deemed as a big red target by people she didn't know and people she knew too much. She was constantly shot at; arrows stuck off her back, blood dripped down to her calves. Scars bloomed beautifully into a fist and heart, into names that she will not forget, she will always say. So, Salma screamed, so loudly, until her throat bled, "I will overcome. My brother, mother, they will overcome. My sister, father, friends, and enemies, they will overcome. I will not be shackled by the hands of society, not by bone-white hands, never. I will not be quiet."

Hurt and pain, blood and scars, can water pretty red roses just as good as water. In fact, even better. All you need is sunlight, love, and care for the rose to grow, for the bud to bloom. All you need to do is heal. So, heal for me and you. As a flower bud, you are hope, change, and resilience personified. You are the children of people who stomped their feet and stood their ground. Your roots are planted, holding onto the earth tight.

"As a flower bud," you say, "we will overcome."

Flower buds. We will overcome.

DELILAH

OBELYN SMITH

I remember eight. Scissors slick in my clumsy hands. I stared down a legion in that mirror. My reflection the snap of blade against blade, skin pulling with desperation as the last of the hair fell. I remember hatred. Clumps of it like black sheep's wool, culled to keep some child's dreams. I remember dreaming that silk ringlets might grow back, not the wads of cotton curling from my head, heavy enough to cut. I remember hoping scissors would be all that God need give me to strike it down, tame it into something lovable. Eight more long years before I remember: It is enough to love myself.

BLACK EXPERIENCE

Afro-futurism serves as a bridge from the past to the future by exploring: I was, I am, and I will be.

HEAVENLY JUSTICE
MAJESTE PHILLIP

Church bells ringing on a serene Sunday morning

The choir singers painted with every color in God's pallet

Singing various stanzas, harmonies, bridges, and refrains,

yet each enveloped within the same unanimous melody

They sing "justice for you may not look like the same
kind of justice I need

But impartial justice served to one, means justice served
for all humanity"

And just like that freedom is brought to life, baring the
nourishing taste of honey

For once the sweet savoring scent of empathy outweighs
the enticing stench of money

Hate, prejudice, and bias, uprooted from a nation so
called United

Re-envisioning the founding documents where racism
was subliminally invited

Plucking out the thorn-riddled weeds buried beneath a
functioning system predicated on division

We claimed to be a nation under God, but strip him of
his role each time we misconstrue his vision

You see, justice for all would feel a lot like heaven

God created every color in the rainbow

And it's about time we viewed each color as a blessing

No one is blameless, no one is perfect

Yes, racial healing may be uncomfortable, but in the end,
it'll always be worth it

MY BLACK EXPERIENCE
MATEO DEDOMON DJEVI

Growing up a Black kid in America, I had to learn life won't always treat you fairly. When I was younger, and still right now, I have always wondered, what is the point? Why would you discriminate because of the color of someone's skin? It's like discriminating because of someone's hair, or clothes—which, unfortunately, both are other problems in this world. After all these years, although I hear it time and time again—they are here to protect you and keep you safe—I still lower my head around police. My eyes glance down at their guns, and I think within a few moments my life could be over, because of the color of my skin. If my dad is out of the house for too long, I'm afraid he has been pulled over by a racist officer. Racism. When I was younger, it seemed like a dark shadow in the corner of the room, but now it feels like a dark reality that seeps over the sun and covers my life, suffocating me, covering my life with the fear of it. Always there, never leaving.

Racism is a problem that has been in our country for years. We were told to accept it, to not question it, but most of us colored people did. We stood up for ourselves and told our oppressors that we wouldn't be walked over and bullied anymore. We got our freedom, but racism is still here and living. We can't act like we have fully fixed the problem, or that we will have fixed the problem for future generations. We haven't. We are going to have to teach the next generation all we can about the problem. Have the conversations with your kids about racism, tell them about the problems in our society. As a kid myself, I know that we want to know these things. If we have these conversations now, then the problem we may not be able to fix in this generation, we may be able to fix in the next generation.

The thing is, racism has been an idea that has been around for hundreds of years. If an idea has been around for as long as it has, it can be incredibly difficult to stamp out, especially if important political figures are promoting it in even the smallest of ways. My dad has always told me to be proud of who I am and of the color of my skin. He introduced me to prominent black figures such as MLK Jr. and Obama. He has explained to me why the colored people of this world are viewed as dangerous thugs, or criminals. It's the image of Black people, that we are dangerous, all of us, that is a center pillar of racism. People have no reason to think this about us, to judge us by the color of our skin. And yet they still do. Why? Again, what is the point of racism? How can our society go on and continue to prosper with this dark secret hiding just beneath the surface? This country seems content just sweeping anything under the rug, as long as it benefits racism to stay under there. We can't continue to prosper as a people if this problem stays in communities all around the country.

The actions a person can do when they are driven by racism is horrible. Like MLK Jr. said, "Injustice anywhere is a threat to justice everywhere." Slavery first started in 1619, when the Portuguese ship São João Bautista hauled captive Africans from Angola to North America. Slavery was abolished in 1865 and years after that, all the slaves were free. In my mind, racism has continued slavery. Racism is the slavery of the mind, enslaving the mind in the idea that white people are superior to colored people. Of course we have the enslavers, which are racist people and groups, and we have the enslaved, which is everyone who has ever experienced racism.

Another problem is, if you're Black, you can't just go around thinking everyone who is white is racist. My mom is white, and she is one of the nicest persons you will ever meet. If we believe all white people are racist, then it's no different from racist people thinking all Black people are dangerous, and that turns racism on its head and starts it again in a different way than before. We don't seek to be more powerful than white people in the world, we just want to be treated with the same respect and dignity. I hope this paragraph has inspired you to stand up and advocate for your rights. If it hasn't, I hope the rest of this book will. I believe that if we show racists we aren't going to be bullied anymore, then they will back down. Thank you, and Black Lives Matter.

I AM...
SAMIRA CREWS

I am cute and I have beautiful skin
Nobody can have this skin and beautiful face

I come from Saint Paul and Rondo Library

What you see when you look at me is I am a role model
What you don't see is playing around

Healing is health and kindness

Freedom is to be free from this cruel world
Justice is freedom and amen and putting your fist up for people who agree with what the bad people do

My one wish for the world is police to stop killing people they're not supposed to kill like Amir Locke.

I AM...
CHARLES WHITE

I am football and I play it.
I come from Maplewood, Minnesota.

When they look at me, they see a person that likes basketball.

What they do not see is that I am an energetic person.

Health means to me to be able to have the choice to do what you want.

Justice means to me to do what you want. Equality.

My one wish for the world is that everyone is good.

I AM...
DOMINIQUE WHITE

I am independent and artistic.

I come from my mom's stomach.

When someone sees me, they see an independent girl who is grown to be a woman.

What people don't see in me is how smart I really am.

Healing means you could heal from an injury or heal from something depressing that happened in the past.

My one wish for the world is that everyone would follow Jesus and hope to follow Jesus' example.

I AM...
XAVIER WASHINGTON

I am a football player.

I come from Minnesota.

In me you see helpful.

In me you don't see the great football player.

Healing is not hurting people with fists or words, and helping people.

Freedom is not being trapped or held back by anyone or thing and being able to speak and show your mind.

Justice is not being judged or called out for their skin color or who they are.

My wish for the world is that people believe in and love God and love themselves.

I AM...
AMELIA CALLENDAR

I am a biracial little girl who has the biggest future ahead of her life.

I come from a world so big that you'll never really know if you'll do anything in life.

When you look at me, you see a young African American and Cambodian child who has a lot of confidence in herself and others when it comes to following her dreams.

What you don't see is all the negative thoughts and barriers that Aniyah has overcome because she doesn't let those tiny things overpower who she really is.

What stresses me out is when people have to be so ignorant and listen to what other people say when they have no talk or say in what other people do.

I take care of myself by letting my body decide on what's right for me and what's wrong for me and my body.

Healing, to me, is to let my body be a sponge and soak up all the stuff that's good for my body and all the stuff that's bad for my body and let it disappear.

Justice, to me, is to be fair, to have peace, for kids of different races to all be friends because they aren't different in too many ways. For our skin color to not have to take over who we really are.

Freedom, to me, is to be free, not to have people make fun of you because you are this color or have people make fun of you because you talk like this or you eat like that.

None of that would happen if we really had freedom in our state, our country, or our world.

My wish for my community is that everyone is healthy, fed, and in a safe place because no one ever (including me) would want to be in a place where they aren't healthy, fed, or safe. I know some people can't control it, but for those people who can't, I want to be the person who makes sure they can.

I wish that my community has a great future ahead of them because the future is what you should focus on and not the past. Your past can only make you want to go back to it, but for some people, they might want to look back at their past because their present isn't the same as their past, but even if that is the case, you can always have a future to change.

SUN AND SHINE
AZELIA CALENDAR

I am Azelia. I come from Minnesota. When you look at me, you see a leader, and what you don't see is perfectness. What stresses me out is when people don't listen to a word I'm saying. I take care of myself by getting ready to go somewhere. Healing, to me, is like peace. Justice, to me, is beautiful. Freedom, to me, is special. My wish for my community is they will never, ever give up on anything.

ABOUT ME & WHAT I THINK
KAHTONA MOORE

I am Kahtona. I come from upstate New York. When you look at me you see a tall light skin girl with curly hair and brown eyes. What you don't see is a short blonde girl with blue eyes. Something that stresses me out is my brother losing something. I take care of myself by doing skin care and taking time for myself. Healing to me is never giving up and your heart is healing from whatever you're going through. Justice to me is basically like freedom or you get what you want. Freedom to me is free and you can do whatever. My wish for my community is to do better...why violence?

WHAT I SEE
CHYNNA FOSTER

I am Chynna Foster. I am 11 years old. I am a 5th grader. I come from Chicago. I come from St. Paul. When you look at me, you see a young Black woman. When you look at me, you see a 5th grader. I am not a disrespectful girl. What stresses me out is when people don't listen. I take care of myself by brushing my teeth and washing my face and taking a shower and cleaning my room. Healing, to me, is staying away from negativity and not letting people get to me. Justice, to me, is Black people not getting locked up by white cops. Freedom, to me, is people not being racist to little kids. My wish for this community is for people to take care of it and not litter.

I AM...
DACARRI LOWERY

I am Dacarri

I come from Chicago

When you look at me, you see a kid

What you don't see is a kind kid

What stresses me out is my mom because she works so hard

I take care of myself by helping myself

Healing, to me, is saying sorry and giving a hug

Justice, to me, is finding people who don't follow the law

Freedom, to me, is when people aren't being racist

My wish for my community is to be accepted

I AM...
NAY'LYIAH DAVIS

I am a Beautiful Black Queen

I come from Saint Paul, Minnesota

When you look at me, you see my hair and my beautiful Black face

What you don't see is my heart, my brain

What stresses me out is when my baby sister is yelling for no reason

I take care of myself by taking showers and cleaning myself

Healing, to me, is when you are hurting and you sit at home and rest your body

Justice, to me, is treating people how you want to be treated

Freedom, to me, is to let someone be free in the world

My wish for my community is to stay safe and have a good life while you stay out of drama

WHO I AM
DAZARIAH ELLIS

I am smart, strong, helpful, honorable,
fantastic, hard-working, creative,
myself. I come from a strong, Black,
creative, helpful, hard-working, nice,
respectful, beautiful, caring, mature,
responsible, inspiring woman who
is a leader. When you look at me,
you see an inspiration, creativity,
expression, tough, powerful, strong,
responsible girl. What you don't see
is a lazy, mean, sad, annoying, bossy
girl. What stresses me out is being
bothered. Being bullied. Getting talked
about. Fighting. I take care of myself
by taking baths, cleaning my clothes,
cleaning my face, being independent,
cooking, and learning. Healing, to me,
is helping poor people and cleaning
up litter, helping people in need build
new and helpful things. Justice, to me,
is people being true. People accepting
fate. People choosing to do the right
things. People who did bad things are
disciplined. Freedom, to me, is being
able to do what you want no matter
your religion or your skin. Being able
to wear what you want either gender.
My wish for my community is we all
do something to help people. We all
clean our town. We all are equal and
fair to other people.

LEADERSHIP CHALLENGE:

Be a Drum Major for Justice

Rev. Dr. Martin Luther King, Jr.'s vision of the "Drum Major" focuses on the interconnectedness of service and leadership.

TO BE A LEADER
NAH'LIYAH DAVIS

Dr. King's words, to me, mean to be a better person and have better thoughts and to make a lot of people feel better. It helps me by helping other people when they have accidents and when people are mean to them.

To be a leader, to me, means not to be a follower and to mind your own business and not get into stuff so you don't get in trouble.

Dr. King has inspired me by being a good person, and he's inspired me to not be a person like these other people out here and to be a really nice person to people and my family.

DR. MARTIN LUTHER KING, JR.
ABIGAIL MUTUA

Martin Luther King, Jr. was a civil rights leader and he spoke the gospel. He fought for freedom. He said that he didn't care that he would lose all his stuff when he died, but he would hope, when he died, that we would all have equal rights. He never stopped fighting for freedom. It was really sad when he died. He was such a great man. He made a speech called I Have a Dream, and it talked about equal rights. We all miss him.

Dr. King, Jr. stood for peace, love, and freedom. He told Black people they can be anything they want to be, and that's why we had a Black president. Dr. King, Jr. inspired so many people and that's why we love him. Dr. King, Jr. kept going and never gave up.

I AM INSPIRED BY DR. KING, JR....
ANIYAH STEWART

I am inspired by Dr. King, Jr. because he lets us know and shows us that we can be who we want and live the dream we always wanted to live. He shows us that life isn't always about money or how smart you are. It's about the things and dreams you accomplish on your own. He shows us that it's not always about the love that you get or if you get recognized, it's about the love you give others and the fact that you are able to recognize others and the changes they make for the world. He shows us that life isn't always about if you're "poor" or "rich," because at the end of the day you are you and always you. That's the best part of you—you are a dream. A person. You are something, and nobody can ever tell you that you're not, because you are what you want to be.

DRUM MAJOR INSTINCT
GABRIEL HINKLE

I am inspired by Martin Luther King, Jr. He inspired me because he said you don't need to be a genius to make a change—all you need is a heart full of grace. Now what it is to be a leader means not to give up, keep going, because there is a good prize at the end. So don't give up. I can't wait to see you at the end.

DRUM MAJOR INSTINCT
KHAMANI JENKINS

Dr. King, Jr.'s words mean I am a special kid and I can do good. I can get a good job. I can make good choices, I can have fun, I can be great. I am wonderful. I can have a great heart, and I can have a great life.

DRUM MAJOR INSTINCT
JAZAYA ALEXANDER PAYTON

Dr. King, Jr. is a man who stayed believing in me and you, for rights for white kids and Black kids to play together. First, he went on a movement, the Civil Rights Movement, because he thought Black people got treated wrong. But he and people got chased by police dogs. But he saved the kids and he kept doing this, and white people helped too. He went to jail, and it started the boycott where Rosa Parks did not want to give up her seat. She went to jail too. He got out of jail. He did a speech called I Have a Dream. The government told someone to shoot him. But we still celebrate his birthday. Never stop believing Black Lives Matter.

DRUM MAJOR INSTINCT
ZYMIR HOPKINS

Dr. King, Jr. liked to love people. He loved everybody in the world. He spread the love to everybody, even knowing that they were mean to him. He loved God, he loves you, and he loved everybody, all pets, all everything. He appreciated his life. But I wish I could see him.

I can spread the love to everybody though. At least he had peace in him to spread around. He never stopped believing in himself. But he did quit; he was scaring the white people.

REFLECTION GUIDE

These writing prompts can serve as a guide for community building. Gather a group of students, friends, and family members to pause, reflect, and grow.

I AM

I am...

I come from...

When you look at me, you see...

What you don't see is...

What stresses me out...

I take care of myself by...

Healing, to me, is...

Justice, to me, is...

Freedom, to me, is...

My wish for my community...

This writing prompt was provided by the Irreducible Grace Foundation.

DRUM MAJOR INSTINCT

What are the leadership characteristics of a drum major for justice? How can a drum major build and sustain social change?

"If you want to be important—wonderful. If you want to be recognized—wonderful. If you want to be great—wonderful. But recognize that he who is greatest among you shall be your servant. That's a new definition of greatness. And this morning, the thing that I like about it: by giving that definition of greatness, it means that everybody can be great, because everybody can serve."

-Dr. Martin Luther King, Jr.

Made in the USA
Monee, IL
22 November 2022

18306105R00021